Sydney and the Sloth

(A Book About Depression)

Written by
Holly Duhig

Illustratred by
Drue Rintoul

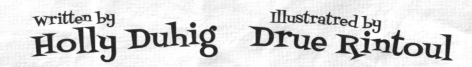

HEALTHY
MINDS

BookLife
PUBLISHING

©2018
BookLife Publishing
King's Lynn
Norfolk PE30 4LS

A catalogue record for this
book is available from the
British Library.

ISBN: 978-1-78637-358-8

Written by:
Holly Duhig

Edited by:
Madeline Tyler

Designed by:
Drue Rintoul

With grateful thanks to Place2Be for their endorsement of this series.

These titles have been developed to support teachers and
school counsellors in exploring pupils' mental health, and have
been reviewed and approved by the clinical team at Place2Be,
the leading national children's mental health charity.

Something to think about...

While you're reading, have a think about these questions:

Sydney feels very, very sad. His mum has not been feeling well for a long time. Sometimes she is at home with Sydney, but often she stays at the hospital and Sydney has to stay at his grandma's house.

Now Sydney has a sloth. He doesn't know where Sloth came from or how long he has been with him, but it looks like Sloth is here to stay.

Wherever Sydney goes, his sloth goes too. After a while, Sloth became too tired to walk around by himself. Now Sydney carries Sloth with him on his back.

Sloths are very sleepy creatures. When Sydney goes to bed at his grandma's house, Sloth snoozes on his chest. Sydney wants to keep going to school but Sloth makes it hard to get up in the morning.

Sloths move very slowly and Sydney's sloth is no different. When he comes down for breakfast, Grandma tells Sydney to, "Stop dragging your feet!" Sydney doesn't know how to tell her that it is his sloth that is slowing him down.

Sometimes Sloth gets in the way of Sydney doing the things he wants to do. Sydney used to love reading. He used to read stacks of books! Unfortunately for Sydney, sloths can't read so they get bored of books very quickly.

Because of this, Sloth isn't very helpful at school. Carrying a sloth around makes concentrating on school work very difficult. Sydney used to love getting gold stars on his work but sloths don't care about gold stars. They would rather just go to sleep.

Today, Sydney's teacher, Ms Bell, wants the class to start a new project. "You can choose to work alone or in groups," she says.

Everyone is excited about the project but Sydney just feels bored. "Nobody will want to work with me anyway," Sydney thinks to himself.

Sloth gives Sydney a hug to make him feel better but it's not very comforting. Sloth's hugs feel far too tight and far too warm. "You can work on your own with me," says Sloth.

Sloth won't even leave Sydney alone at lunchtime. When the bell rings and everyone rushes to their feet, Sloth just clings harder to his friend.

Sydney wants to go and play outside but it looks like Sloth has other ideas. Sloths aren't very playful creatures.

Sloth stretches out on the doormat in front of the classroom door. "I don't want to go and play," Sloth sighs, "Let's have a nap instead." Sloth looks bigger and heavier than ever.

Sydney tries to pick Sloth up and pull him out of the way, but Sloth won't budge. He's grown far too heavy and far too floppy.

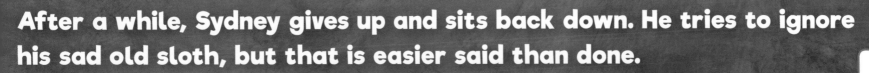

After a while, Sydney gives up and sits back down. He tries to ignore his sad old sloth, but that is easier said than done.

13

Sydney takes out his packed lunch. His grandma has made his favourite sandwiches but today they taste as bland as sand.

Sydney thinks about his mum and his grandma and he starts to cry. Everything feels wrong and Sloth isn't helping one bit.

Suddenly, Sydney hears a loud **SLAM!** It makes him jump. Sloth is flung across the classroom and Sydney looks up to see Ms Bell standing in the spot where Sloth was laying just moments ago.

"What's the matter Sydney?" asks Ms Bell. "I couldn't see you outside in the playground." She sees that Sydney is crying and she hands him a clean, but slightly crumpled, tissue from her pocket.

Sydney tells her all about Sloth while Sloth clings shakily to Sydney. Sloth is suddenly quite scared of Ms Bell.

Sydney tells his teacher all about Sloth and how he won't let him play outside. He tells Ms Bell that he's scared that Sloth will get heavier and heavier until he can never move again.

Ms Bell gives his hand a tight squeeze. She tells him about David, the school counsellor, who is an expert at shrinking big, heavy sloths. "Would you like to go and see him?" she asks.

Sloth still feels very heavy on Sydney's leg. But, with Ms Bell holding his hand, Sydney is able to drag Sloth all the way to the school counsellor's office.

The school counsellor's name is David. David has curly, orange hair and a kind smile. There are lots of things to play with in his office, from building bricks to paper and crayons. David asks Sydney if he'd like to draw his sloth.

Sydney draws Sloth with his big sleepy eyes and sad mouth. He tells David how Sloth makes him feel lonely and tired and it makes him want to cry.

"Sloths love being alone and sleeping all day, but it's not very good for humans," explains David. "When sloths live with humans for too long, they can make their human very sad."

David says that talking about how he feels may help lift Sloth's weight off Sydney's shoulders. So, Sydney tells David all about his mum being poorly and living at Grandmas. "I'm worried she won't get better," Sydney admits.

David gives Sydney a notebook where he can write down how he feels when things are getting to be too much. "This might make it easier to talk about your thoughts and feelings to me and your mum."

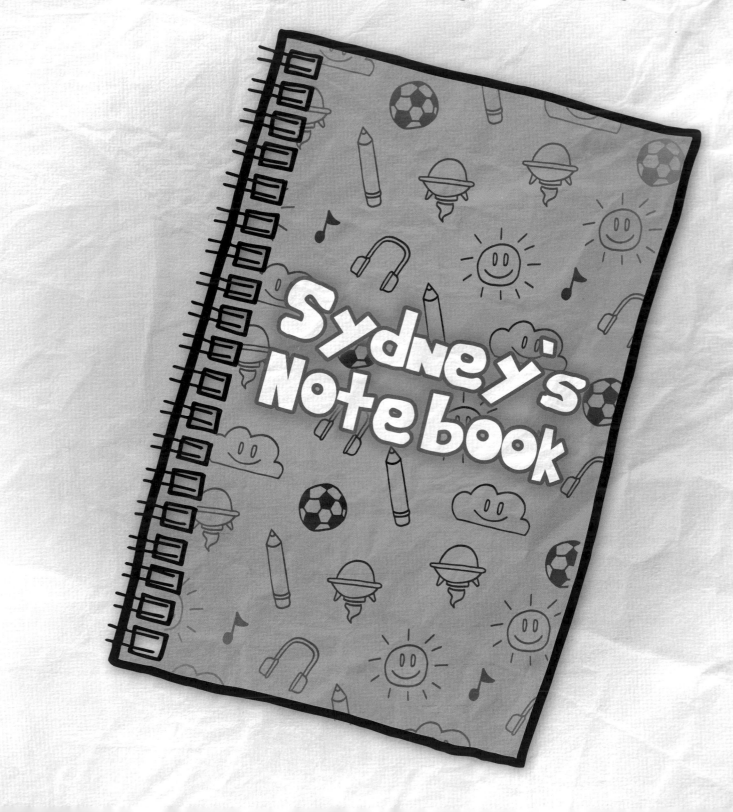

Sloth feels a little lighter every day, and some days Sydney barely notices Sloth is there at all. Although Sloth still feels heavy sometimes, Sydney now feels strong enough to carry him, with the help of David, the super sloth-shrinker!

More Information

Everyone feels sad from time-to-time but, when someone feels very sad for a long period of time, it is called having depression. Depression is a mental health condition which means it affects your mind. Depression can make you lose interest in the things you love. It can also make you feel bored, tired and unwell.

Depression can be hard to manage but you can get better from it. If you, or someone you know, has been feeling very sad for a long time, talking to someone you trust – like a doctor counsellor, parent or carer – is the first step to getting help.